I would like to dedicate this book my husband Peter and my sons Steven and Shane for putting up with me reading my stories to them every time I changed a few lines.

To my mum Bridget and sister Bernie, who have always been there when I've needed them.

Thank you all so much for the support and encouragement you have given me!

xxx

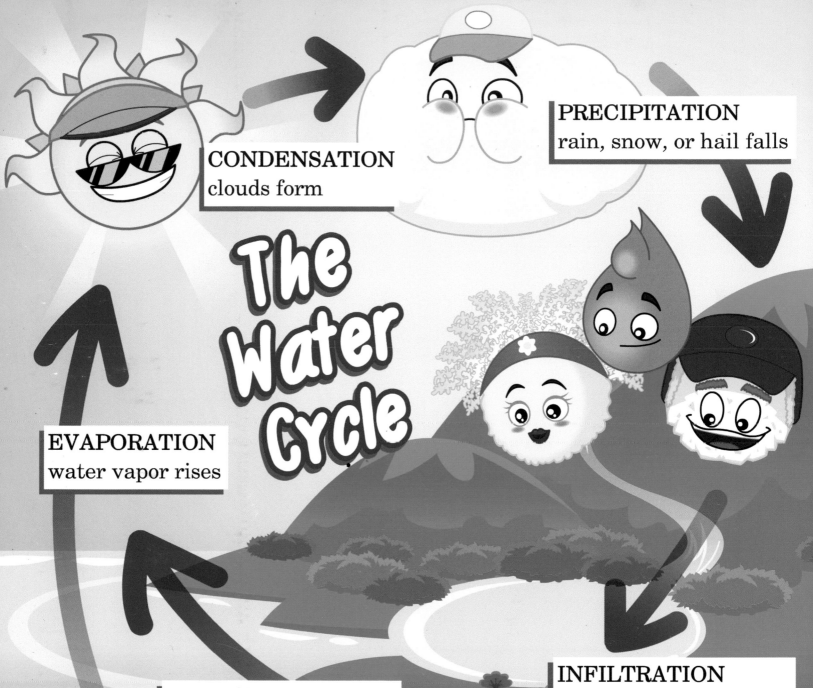

CONDENSATION
clouds form

PRECIPITATION
rain, snow, or hail falls

The Water Cycle

EVAPORATION
water vapor rises

TRANSPIRATION
water vapor is released
into the air through
plant leaves

INFILTRATION
water soaks the ground

More characters and stories to come,
full of fun and adventures from...

www.theweatherbies.co.uk

The Splashing Sunbeams all shout, "HURRAY!"
When Colin Cloud said they have won.
The Pollutants learnt about the water cycle,
and *The Weatherbies* had lots of fun.

Colin Cloud replied, "OK!"
As he changed his shape again.
Harry Hail shouts, "Are you a bicycle?"
And wins the last point of the game.

The Pollutants are very impressed,
but now it's time for them to go.
"Make another shape Colin Cloud!"
Shouted little Flow Snow.

Sammy Sun shines his bright warm glow,
and the puddles all start to dry.
The water cycle never stops,
as the moisture rises into the sky.

Ronny said, "Water is very important,
it keeps everything alive.
Water falls as rain or snow,
Without it Earth wouldn't survive!"

Ronny Rain sprays his water,
leaving puddles all over the ground.
The little flowers all lift their heads,
as the water comes splashing down.

Colin Cloud's cheeks are getting red,
he's feeling full and fit to burst.
He shouts out, "Quick Ronny, turn on the rain,
so we can quench these little plant's thirst!"

"When Colin's too full, I turn on the rain,
that's the job for me!
I return the water for collection,
back to the rivers, lakes, land and sea!"

"When Sammy Sun shines his bright warm glow,
moisture rises into the sky!
Then Colin Cloud catches it,
Leaving the ground nice and dry."

"Is the water cycle like a bicycle?"
Susie Smog asks Ronny Rain.
"No! It's the journey water takes as it circulates."
Ronny Rain starts to explain.

"Where did all the puddles go?"
Asks Olly Oil looking confused.
"It's the water cycle." Replied Harry Hail,
"The water keeps getting reused!"

"What are you playing?" Asks Lisa Litter,
dropping rubbish all over the ground.
"I bet it's silly!" Shouts Susie Smog,
as she puffs smoke all around.

Sammy Sun is shining bright,
and the Pollutants soon feel nice and dry.
Colin Cloud catches the moisture,
as it rises, up into the sky.

Just then the naughty Pollutant's appear,
in a cloud of thick black smoke.
Ronny Rain turns and splashes them,
Giving them all a good soak.

WHOOOOSH!

Willy Wind's very excited,
because Colin Cloud looks like a kite.
He wins a point for the Colourful Winds,
when he gets the answer right.

Colin Cloud changes shape again,
he looks like a big cream bun.
Sammy Sun starts to laugh and shout,
"This game is so much FUN!"

Ronny Rain jumps with a splash,
spraying water up into the air.
He wins a point for the Splashing Sunbeams,
when he shouts, "Are you a teddy bear?"

The game can start now the teams are picked,
and Colin Cloud's ready to go.
They all watch as he makes a shape,
"Are you an elephant?" Giggles Flo Snow.

Colin Cloud said, "Look at me as I change shape,
and shout out what you see.
If you get it right, you win a point,
so just keep watching me!"

When everyone gets to the park,
they start to pick the teams.
Rosie's team is called Colourful Winds,
and Ronny's is Splashing Sunbeams.

Harry Hail bounced in through the gate,
waved his hand and shouted, "Hello!"
With a flurry, a skip and a shake of her bag,
he's followed by little Flo Snow.

Rosie Rainbow is on a swing,
and asks if she can play.
"Yes, you can!" replied Colin Cloud,
"The others are on their way!"

It wasn't long till their friends turned up,
ready to play and have fun.
Willy Wind blew into the park,
followed by a bright Sammy Sun.

WHOOOOSH!

Colin Cloud rolls down to the Park,
with his best friend, Ronny Rain.
Ronny Rain said, "If our friends come along,
we can play making shapes again!"

Colin Cloud loves making shapes,
it's one of his favourite games.
Sometimes he's a cat, a hat or a mouse,
and sometimes he looks like a train.